# Times To

Scholastic Children's Books
Euston House,
24 Eversholt Street,
London NW1 1DB, UK

A division of Scholastic Ltd
London • New York • Toronto • Sydney • Auckland
Mexico City • New Delhi • Hong Kong

Book packaging by Blooberry Design

Published in the UK by Scholastic Ltd, 2017

ISBN 978 1 4071 6614 8

Printed in Italy

2 4 6 8 10 9 7 5 3

Papers used by Scholastic Children's Books are made from wood grown in sustainable forests.

www.scholastic.co.uk

# Welcome to the Disney Learning Programme!

Children learn best when they are having fun!

The **Disney Learning Workbooks** are an engaging way for your child to develop maths skills along with fun characters from the wonderful world of Disney.

The **Disney Learning Workbooks** are carefully levelled to present new challenges to developing learners. This workbook has been designed to support the National Curriculum for Mathematics at Key Stage 1. It includes activities to help your child to practise skills learned at school, which can be consolidated in a relaxed home setting with parental support. Stickers and a range of number and multiplication activities related to the film *Beauty and the Beast* ensure that children have fun while learning.

Learning the times tables requires your child to bring together many skills. By the end of Key Stage 1, children are expected to be able to recall and use the facts from the 2, 3, 5 and 10 times tables with ease. Doing this will take time to master: practice will be crucial in helping your child to become fluent in these times tables. Once these become effortless, your child will be more confident in manipulating numbers when wanting to solve other maths problems.

This book includes 'Take a Break' sections, which are fun activities related to *Beauty and the Beast*. Keep each practice session short and fun, remembering to help your child to read the instructions so it is clear what to do before starting.

## Have fun with the Disney Learning Programme!

Developed in conjunction with Charlotte Raby, educational consultant

# Let's Learn
# Times Tables

In this book, you will find lots of activities to help you learn and practise the 2, 3, 5 and 10 x tables.

You will learn to use a number line to work out the patterns of a times table. You will find number lines on lots of pages in this book.

+2  +2  +2

0  2  4  6  8  10  12  14  16  18  20

Learning your times tables is fun. Once you know the times table facts, you can be confident when you work out number problems.

## Helpful tips

- Find somewhere quiet to work.

- Read the questions very carefully. If you are not sure what to do, ask a grown-up to help you read the instructions.

- Learn a times table thoroughly before trying to learn the next one.

You will also use arrays to help you work out the times tables. Arrays are pictures we can use to help us see the groups of numbers in a times table.

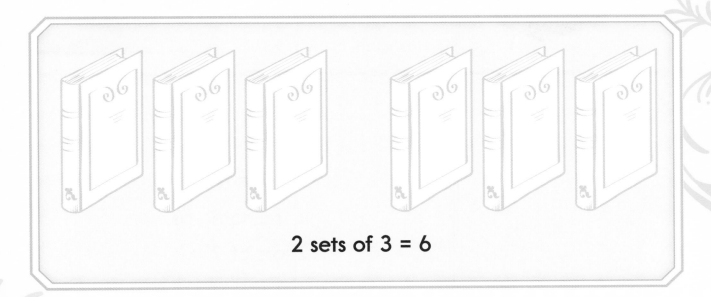

2 sets of 3 = 6

Another way of thinking about times tables is to see them as adding again and again.

2 x 3 is just the same as 2 + 2 + 2.

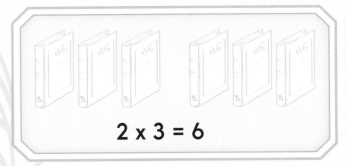

2 x 3 = 6

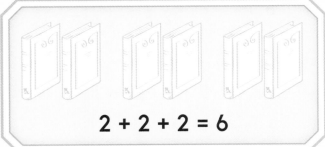

2 + 2 + 2 = 6

You can work out the answers this way when you multiply, until you know your times tables well.

Can you count in 2s? Use the number line to help Mrs Potts jump along 2 numbers at a time to reach Chip.

0  1  2  3  4  5  6  7  8  9  10  11  12  13  14  15  16  17  18  19  20

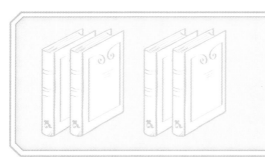

2 + 2 = 4

**is the same as**

2 lots of 2 = 4

Work out these number sentences using the number line to help you. Write your answers in the boxes.

**a**   2 + 2 + 2 = ◯

**b**   2 + 2 + 2 + 2 = ◯

**c**   2 + 2 + 2 + 2 + 2 = ◯

Work out these number sentences
using the arrays to help you.

**a**

2 + 2 + 2 = ☐

is the same as 3 lots of 2 = ☐

is the same as 2 x 3 = ☐

**b**

2 + 2 + 2 + 2 = ☐

is the same as 4 lots of 2 = ☐

is the same as 2 x 4 = ☐

**c**

2 + 2 + 2 + 2 + 2 = ☐

is the same as 5 lots of 2 = ☐

is the same as 2 x 5 = ☐

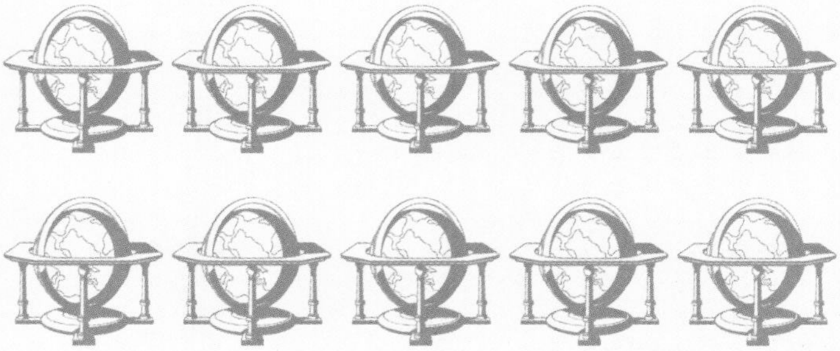

# Let's Learn the 2 x Table

Belle loves to learn new things. This is the 2 x table.

It's easy to learn – just follow the 5 steps as you fill in the 'You try' column.

1 **Look** at the number sentence.

2 **Say** it out loud.

3 **Cover** it with your hand or a piece of paper.

4 **Write** the number sentence from memory.

5 **Check** your answer.

| The 2 x table | You try... |
|---|---|
| 1 x 2 = 2 | |
| 2 x 2 = 4 | |
| 3 x 2 = 6 | |
| 4 x 2 = 8 | |
| 5 x 2 = 10 | |
| 6 x 2 = 12 | |
| 7 x 2 = 14 | |
| 8 x 2 = 16 | |
| 9 x 2 = 18 | |
| 10 x 2 = 20 | |

Circle only the numbers that are in the 2 x table. Then connect the numbers on the glass however you like to create a pattern.

1

2    3

4    5    6

7    8    9

10   11   12

13   14   15

16   17   18

19   20

# Let's Double

Cogsworth is seeing double! Doubling is the same as multiplying by 2.

Add stickers until you have double the number you had at the start.

a

b

c

d

e

Help Plumette double the numbers on the dice. Do this by drawing the correct number of spots. Then write out the number sentences. The first one has been done for you.

    2 + 2 = 4

**a**     ◯ + ◯ = ◯

**b**     ◯ + ◯ = ◯

**c**     ◯ + ◯ = ◯

**d**     ◯ + ◯ = ◯

# Take a Break

Starting at the red dot, join the dots in groups
of 2 to reveal who never spills tea …
or secrets.

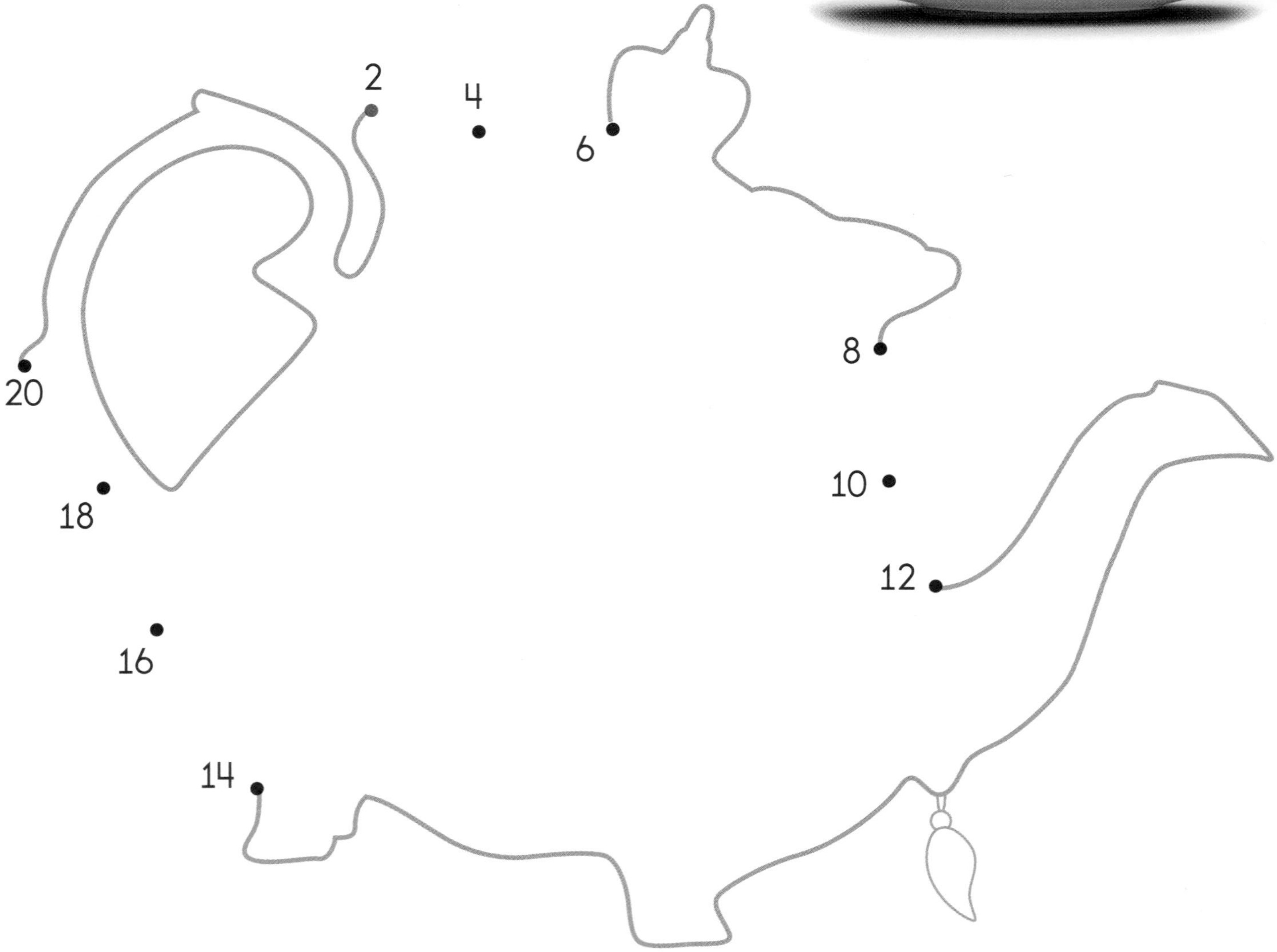

2

4

6

8

20

18

10

16

12

14

Whose silhouettes are these?
Find the sticker that matches each image.

Can you count in 3s?
Use the number line to help Chapeau
hop 3 numbers at a time.

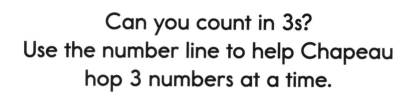

0 1 2 3 4 5 6 7 8 9 10 11 12 13 14 15 16 17 18 19 20 21 22 23 24 25 26 27 28 29 30

Each candlestick has 3 candles. Work out these
number sentences using the number line to help you.
Write your answers in the boxes.

**a**     3 + 3 + 3 = ☐

**b**     3 + 3 + 3 + 3 = ☐

**c**   3 + 3 + 3 + 3 + 3 = ☐

Belle loves numbers as well as words. This is the 3 x table. Now let's learn the 3 x table.

It's easy to learn – just follow the 5 steps as you fill in the 'You try' column.

1 **Look** at the number sentence.

2 **Say** it out loud.

3 **Cover** it with your hand or a piece of paper.

4 **Write** the number sentence from memory.

5 **Check** your answer.

| The 3 x table | You try... |
|---|---|
| 1 x 3 = 3 | |
| 2 x 3 = 6 | |
| 3 x 3 = 9 | |
| 4 x 3 = 12 | |
| 5 x 3 = 15 | |
| 6 x 3 = 18 | |
| 7 x 3 = 21 | |
| 8 x 3 = 24 | |
| 9 x 3 = 27 | |
| 10 x 3 = 30 | |

# Let's Make Sets of 3

Add the missing stickers to show the following number sentences. Write the total in the box each time.

**a**

3 x 3 = ◯

**b**

3 x 4 = ◯

**c**

3 x 5 = ◯

Belle is as beautiful as the roses that grow
in the Beast's garden. Write the missing numbers
in the roses to complete the 3 x table.

15

6

___

___

___

___

___

___

21

27

# Let's Count in 5s

Let's count in 5s. Use the number line to help Cogsworth jump along 5 numbers at a time.

+5          +5

0  1  2  3  4  5  6  7  8  9  10  11  12  13  14  15  16  17  18  19  20  21  22  23  24

Work out these number sentences using the number line to help you. Write your answers in the boxes.

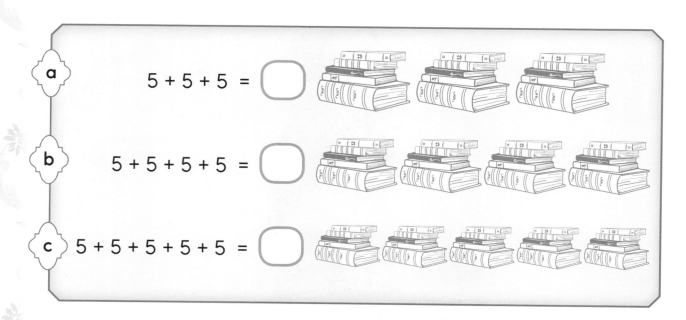

a)   5 + 5 + 5 = ◯

b)   5 + 5 + 5 + 5 = ◯

c)   5 + 5 + 5 + 5 + 5 = ◯

1 **Look** at the number sentence.

2 **Say** it out loud.

3 **Cover** it with your hand or a piece of paper.

4 **Write** the number sentence from memory.

5 **Check** your answer.

Belle always wants to learn more. Here is the 5 x table.

Numbers in the 5 x table always end in 5 or 0.

Follow the five steps as you fill in the 'You try' column.

25 26 27 28 29 30 31 32 33 34 35 36 37 38 39 40 41 42 43 44 45 46 47 48 49 50

| The 5 x table | You try... |
|---|---|
| 1 x 5 = 5 | |
| 2 x 5 = 10 | |
| 3 x 5 = 15 | |
| 4 x 5 = 20 | |
| 5 x 5 = 25 | |
| 6 x 5 = 30 | |
| 7 x 5 = 35 | |
| 8 x 5 = 40 | |
| 9 x 5 = 45 | |
| 10 x 5 = 50 | |

# Take a Break

Look at the value of the items and use them to complete the number sentences below. Then fill in the answers. The first one has been done for you.

 = 2    = 3    = 5    = 10

  ( 5 ) x  ( 3 ) = ( 15 )

**a**   ( ) x   ( ) = ( )

**b**   ( ) x   ( ) = ( )

**c**   ( ) x   ( ) = ( )

**d**   ( ) x  ( ) = ( )

Can you name these characters?
Look at the pictures, then complete
the crossword.

## DOWN

1. 
2. 

## ACROSS

2. 
3. 
4. 
5.

# Let's Learn the 5 x Table

Belle is never happier than when she is learning something new. Circle only the numbers that are in the 5 x table.

Remember, numbers in the 5 x table always end in 5 or 0.

50

36

10

8

2

5       21

40

20

15

Now add more rose stickers so that
each section of the rose bush has 5 roses.

How many roses are there altogether? ( 6 ) x ( 5 ) = ( )

**Mrs Potts and Chip are setting tables for a special dinner.**

Finish the number sentence, then draw more knives
and forks to match the total.

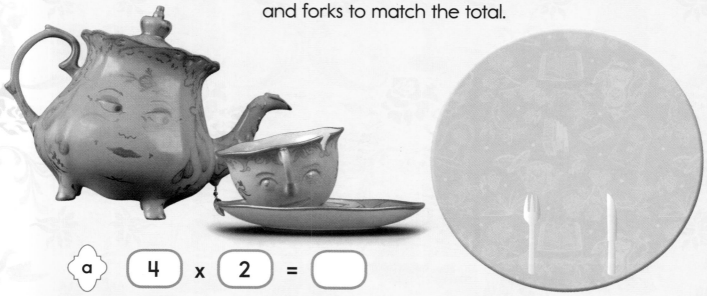

**a**  $4 \times 2 = \boxed{\phantom{00}}$

This time, draw more knives, forks and spoons to
match the number sentence.

**b**  $6 \times 3 = \boxed{\phantom{00}}$

Page 10

Page 16

Page 13

Page 23

Page 26

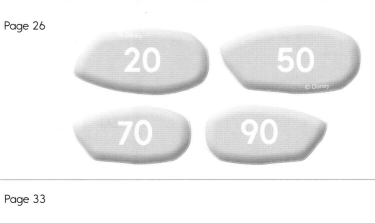

Page 33

Pages 40–41

On this page, each guest needs a knife, fork, spoon, plate and cup. Write the total and draw the missing things.

c  5  x  5  =  ☐

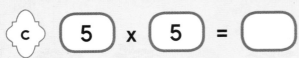
Be our guest!

What would you like to eat for dinner? Draw some delicious food on the plates.

# Let's Count in 10s

| 1 | 2 | 3 | 4 | 5 | 6 | 7 | 8 | 9 | 10 |
|---|---|---|---|---|---|---|---|---|---|
| 11 | 12 | 13 | 14 | 15 | 16 | 17 | 18 | 19 | 20 |
| 21 | 22 | 23 | 24 | 25 | 26 | 27 | 28 | 29 | 30 |
| 31 | 32 | 33 | 34 | 35 | 36 | 37 | 38 | 39 | 40 |
| 41 | 42 | 43 | 44 | 45 | 46 | 47 | 48 | 49 | 50 |
| 51 | 52 | 53 | 54 | 55 | 56 | 57 | 58 | 59 | 60 |
| 61 | 62 | 63 | 64 | 65 | 66 | 67 | 68 | 69 | 70 |
| 71 | 72 | 73 | 74 | 75 | 76 | 77 | 78 | 79 | 80 |
| 81 | 82 | 83 | 84 | 85 | 86 | 87 | 88 | 89 | 90 |
| 91 | 92 | 93 | 94 | 95 | 96 | 97 | 98 | 99 | 100 |

Can you count in 10s?

Colour the numbers in this square that are the products of the 10 x table. The first one has been done for you.

Belle has almost reached the Beast's castle. Help her count how far she walks in distances of 10 metres. Find the stickers to complete the pathway.

100    80    60    40    30    10

b

26

Garderobe has space
to fit **100** items.

Here is the 10 x table.
Numbers in the 10 x table
always end in **0**.

Follow the five steps as you
fill in the 'You try' column.

1 **Look** at the number sentence.

2 **Say** it out loud.

3 **Cover** it with your hand
or a piece of paper.

4 **Write** the number sentence
from memory.

5 **Check** your answer.

| The 10 x table | You try... |
|---|---|
| 1 x 10 = 10 | |
| 2 x 10 = 20 | |
| 3 x 10 = 30 | |
| 4 x 10 = 40 | |
| 5 x 10 = 50 | |
| 6 x 10 = 60 | |
| 7 x 10 = 70 | |
| 8 x 10 = 80 | |
| 9 x 10 = 90 | |
| 10 x 10 = 100 | |

# Finding Sets of 10s

The Beast's castle is surrounded by beautiful rosebushes. Use these arrays to help you work out the following 10 x table multiplication facts. The first one has been done for you.

$$\boxed{3} \times \boxed{10} = \boxed{30}$$

a $\bigcirc \times \bigcirc = \bigcirc$

b $\bigcirc \times \bigcirc = \bigcirc$

c $\bigcirc \times \bigcirc = \bigcirc$

d $\bigcirc \times \bigcirc = \bigcirc$

e $\bigcirc \times \bigcirc = \bigcirc$

**Draw more roses to show the following number sentence.**

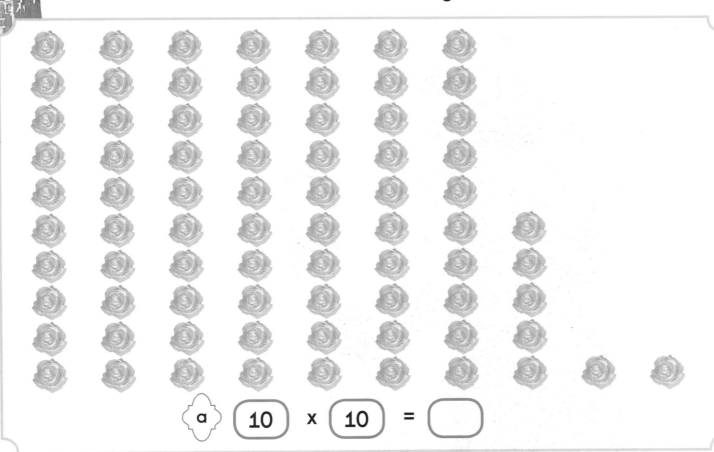

a ( 10 ) x ( 10 ) = (   )

**Draw lines to match the number sentence to its answer each time.**

b ( 3 ) x ( 10 ) =      50

c ( 5 ) x ( 10 ) =      70

d ( 8 ) x ( 10 ) =      30

e ( 10 ) x ( 7 ) =      80

29

Belle looks past the Beast's appearance to see the good in him.

Now it's your turn to look carefully. How many words will you find in the word search on the next page?

They are written forwards, up, down and diagonally.

MULTIPLY    ARRAY      COUNT     TIMES TABLES
EQUALS      DOUBLE     NUMBER    TOTAL

| O | T | J | M | U | L | T | I | P | L | Y | L |
|---|---|---|---|---|---|---|---|---|---|---|---|
| W | E | I | R | W | C | F | S | S | R | X | C |
| O | S | M | M | H | X | O | U | Q | M | T | J |
| S | E | D | M | E | W | A | E | Y | A | O | R |
| Q | S | Z | O | A | S | F | S | N | M | T | A |
| U | L | F | S | U | V | T | L | G | O | A | J |
| P | A | O | E | L | B | C | A | U | F | L | Z |
| A | U | U | F | A | R | L | U | B | S | F | O |
| R | Q | P | S | L | Q | O | E | E | L | Q | C |
| R | E | E | H | A | B | R | E | S | Q | E | M |
| A | C | O | U | N | T | H | Q | O | R | P | S |
| Y | V | N | U | M | B | E | R | P | G | H | L |

# Let's Write Times Table Number Sentences

Belle loves to lose herself in a book. Write out the number sentences using the books in these examples. The first one has been done for you.

$2 \times 3 = 6$

a) $3 \times \boxed{\phantom{0}} = \boxed{\phantom{0}}$

b) $3 \times \boxed{\phantom{0}} = \boxed{\phantom{0}}$

c) $\boxed{\phantom{0}} \times 5 = \boxed{\phantom{0}}$

Another of Belle's favourite things are roses. Place stickers on the bushes to show these number sentences.

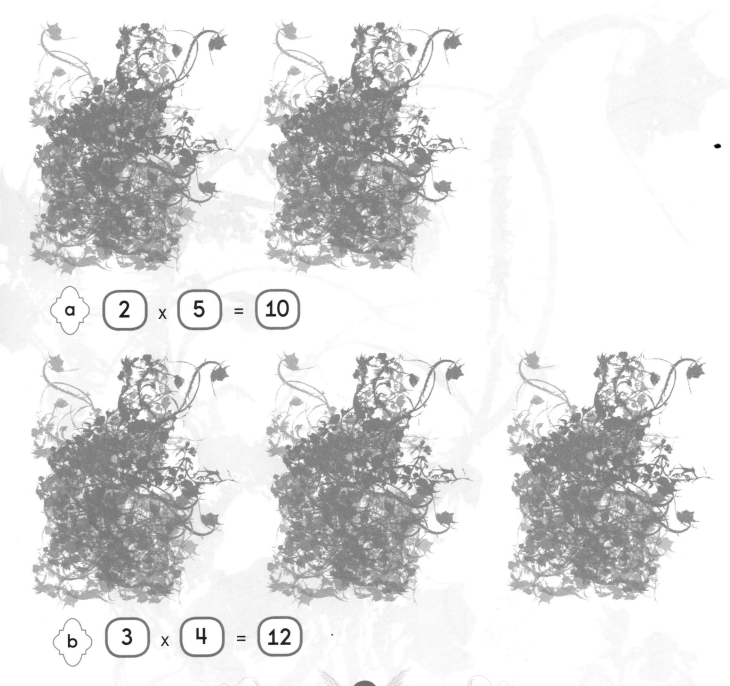

a) 2 x 5 = 10

b) 3 x 4 = 12

# Let's Match Multiplications

Belle and her friends have all lost something
or someone in the Beast's castle.

Draw lines to match each number sentence with the correct
answer in the middle. You'll need to know your
3 x, 5 x and 10 x tables.

4 x 5

3 x 10

2 x 5

5 x 3

6 x 3

10   15   18   20   30

5 x 4

5 x 2

3 x 5

3 x 6

10 x 3

Now write the number sentences for these pictures.
The first one has been done for you.

3 x 5 = 15

a   ( ) x ( 10 ) = ( )

b   ( 3 ) x ( ) = ( )

c   ( ) x ( 6 ) = ( )

# Let's Check the Times Tables We Know

Belle is the most beautiful girl in the village. Fill in the missing numbers on these beautiful necklaces for the 3 x, 5 x and 10 x tables.

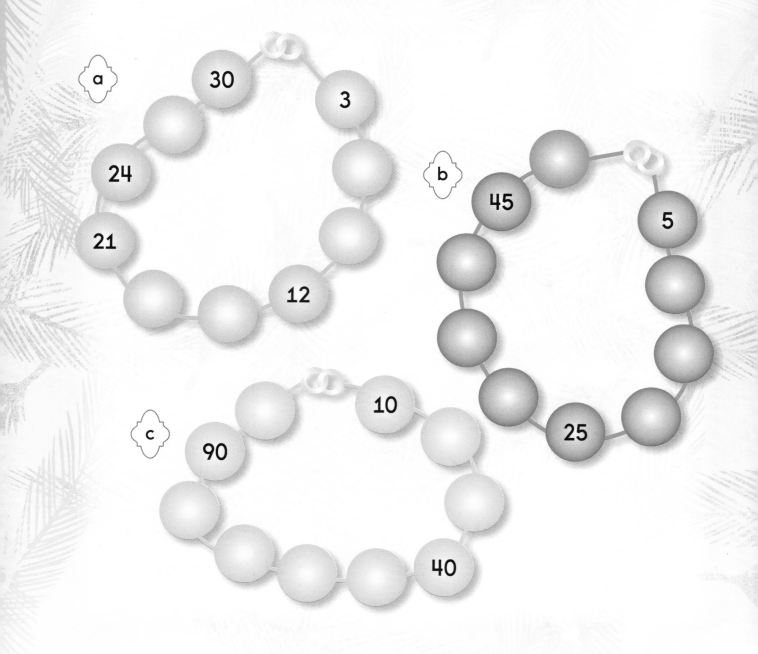

Belle enjoys puzzling things out. Now complete the times table wheels. Multiply the number in each segment by the number in the centre, filling in the boxes as you go. The first two numbers have been done for you each time.

# Let's Play a Game

Before a spell was placed on the Prince, he hosted grand balls and parties at his castle. Imagine that you and a friend have been invited to a ball at the Prince's castle. Which of you will arrive first? Test your times tables skills in this magical game.

You will need a dice, and a counter for each player.

The youngest player starts first.

~

Take it in turns to roll the dice, then move that number of spaces.

~

Answer the multiplication question on the space where you land. If you answer it correctly, stay on that space. If you answer incorrectly, move back 1 space.

~

The first player to reach the Prince's castle is the winner!

10 x 2 =

8 x

1 x 2 =

9 x 10 =

4 x 5 =

START

2 x 2 =

38

FINISH

7 x 3 =

10 x 10 =

7 x 10 =

5 x 4 =

8 x 10 =

0 =

7 x 5 =

2 x 10 =

9 x 2 =

4 x 3 =

5 x 9 =

2 x 3 =

5 x 5 =

x 3 =

3 x 3 =

3 x 5 =

5 x 2 =

3 x 10 =

# Here Are All the Things
# I Can Do

Together, Belle and the Beast can achieve anything.
Place a rose sticker next to the things that you can do!

## I can ...

- use a number line to count in 2s, 3s and 5s

- use repeated addition

- use arrays

## I know ...

- the 2 x table

- the 3 x table

- the 5 x table

- the 10 x table

## I can ...

- write multiplication number sentences

- double a number

- complete a multiplication wheel

# Answers

## Page 6

a. 2 + 2 + 2 = 6
b. 2 + 2 + 2 + 2 = 8
c. 2 + 2 + 2 + 2 + 2 = 10

## Page 7

a.  2 + 2 + 2 = 6
    is the same as 3 lots of 2 = 6
    is the same as 2 x 3 = 6

b.  2 + 2 + 2 + 2 = 8
    is the same as 4 lots of 2 = 8
    is the same as 2 x 4 = 8

c.  2 + 2 + 2 + 2 + 2 = 10
    is the same as 5 lots of 2 = 10
    is the same as 2 x 5 = 10

## Page 9

(Circled numbers)
2, 4, 6, 8, 10, 12, 14, 16, 18, 20

## Page 10

a. 4 x purple roses in total.
b. 8 x yellow feathers in total.
c. 10 x dark pink roses in total.
d. 6 x silver feathers in total.
a. 20 x light pink roses in total.

## Page 11

a. 3 + 3 = 6

b. 1 + 1 = 2

c. 6 + 6 = 12

d. 5 + 5 = 10

## Page 12

## Page 13

## Page 14

a. 3 + 3 + 3 = 9
b. 3 + 3 + 3 + 3 = 12
c. 3 + 3 + 3 + 3 + 3 = 15

## Page 16

a. 3 x 3 = 9        b. 3 x 4 = 12

c. 3 x 5 = 15

## Page 17

3, 6, 9, 12, 15, 18, 21, 24, 27, 30

## Page 18

a. 5 + 5 + 5 = 15
b. 5 + 5 + 5 + 5 = 20
c. 5 + 5 + 5 + 5 + 5 = 25

## Page 20

a. 10 x 5 = 50        c. 2 x 10 = 20
b. 3 x 2 = 6          d. 5 x 2 = 10

## Page 21

```
                                    ¹C
        ²C  O  G  S  W  O  R  T  H
            H                       I
    ³B  E  A  S  T                  P
            P
        ⁴B  E  L  L  E
            A
    ⁵P  L  U  M  E  T  T  E
```

## Page 22

5, 10, 15, 20, 40, 50

## Page 23

6 x 5 = 30 roses altogether.

## Pages 24–25

a. 4 x 2 = 8

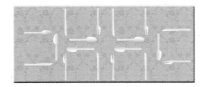

b. 6 x 3 = 18

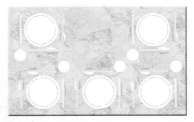

c. 5 x 5 = 25

*Other arrangements of these places are possible.*

## Page 26

a.

| | | | | | | | | | |
|---|---|---|---|---|---|---|---|---|---|
| 1 | 2 | 3 | 4 | 5 | 6 | 7 | 8 | 9 | 10 |
| 11 | 12 | 13 | 14 | 15 | 16 | 17 | 18 | 19 | 20 |
| 21 | 22 | 23 | 24 | 25 | 26 | 27 | 28 | 29 | 30 |
| 31 | 32 | 33 | 34 | 35 | 36 | 37 | 38 | 39 | 40 |
| 41 | 42 | 43 | 44 | 45 | 46 | 47 | 48 | 49 | 50 |
| 51 | 52 | 53 | 54 | 55 | 56 | 57 | 58 | 59 | 60 |
| 61 | 62 | 63 | 64 | 65 | 66 | 67 | 68 | 69 | 70 |
| 71 | 72 | 73 | 74 | 75 | 76 | 77 | 78 | 79 | 80 |
| 81 | 82 | 83 | 84 | 85 | 86 | 87 | 88 | 89 | 90 |
| 91 | 92 | 93 | 94 | 95 | 96 | 97 | 98 | 99 | 100 |

b. Missing stone stickers are: 20, 50, 70 and 90

## Page 28

a. 2 x 10 = 20     b. 6 x 10 = 60

c. 9 x 10 = 90     d. 4 x 10 = 40

e. 1 x 10 = 10

## Page 29

a. 10 x 10 = 100

b. 3 x 10 =       50

c. 5 x 10 =       70

d. 8 x 10 =       30

e. 10 x 7 =       80

## Pages 30–31

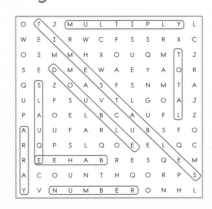

# Answers

## Page 32

a. 3 x 5 = **15**    b. 3 x 7 = **21**    c. 10 x 5 = **50**

## Page 33

a.

b.

## Page 34

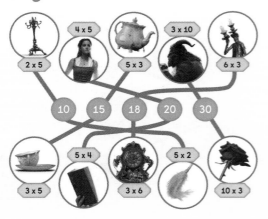

## Page 35

a. 2 x 10 = **20**    b. 3 x 7 = **21**    c. 5 x 6 = **30**

## Page 36

a. 3, 6, 9, 12, 15, 18, 21, 24, 27, 30

b. 5, 10, 15, 20, 25, 30, 35, 40, 45, 50

c. 10, 20, 30, 40, 50, 60, 70, 80, 90, 100

## Page 37

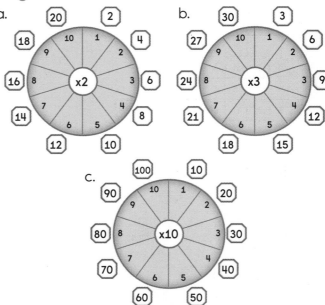

## Pages 38–39

| | |
|---|---|
| 2 x 2 = 4 | 1 x 2 = 2 |
| 2 x 3 = 6 | 10 x 2 = 20 |
| 3 x 3 = 9 | 8 x 5 = 40 |
| 3 x 5 = 15 | 7 x 3 = 21 |
| 5 x 2 = 10 | 10 x 10 = 100 |
| 3 x 10 = 30 | 7 x 10 = 70 |
| 5 x 5 = 25 | 5 x 4 = 20 |
| 2 x 3 = 6 | 8 x 10 = 80 |
| 5 x 9 = 45 | |
| 4 x 3 = 12 | |
| 9 x 2 = 18 | |
| 2 x 10 = 20 | |
| 7 x 5 = 35 | |
| 6 x 10 = 60 | |
| 4 x 5 = 20 | |
| 9 x 10 = 90 | |

It takes time to really master the times tables, which is why we start with the ones that are the simplest to remember. Children will have learned about counting and addition in school. They will understand how numbers increase and have higher value as they go further up the number line. You will need to help your child recall this prior knowledge when you do the times tables together.

## Use physical objects to help your child

Initially, help your child to understand multiplication as 'sets of' a number. Use buttons, counters, blocks or other toys to make sets. Make 3 sets of 5 objects. Ask your child how to work out how many objects there are altogether. Agree that this could work by:

- counting all the objects
- adding up each set of objects
- using the 3 x table to work out the answer.

Work together to try each method. You may want to use a number line to help with the times table method. Do you get the same result each time?

Ask your child to guess which is the quickest way to find out the answer. You want your child to understand that each method comes up with the same answer. Over time, as children become more confident, they will start to use the quickest method to get the answer.

# More Activities to Share with Your Child

## Chanting times tables

It can be fun to chant times tables – honestly! Make a rhythm to help you keep in time and make clapping, patting or clicking patterns to add to the fun. Practise saying the numbers: 2, 4, 6, 8, 10 and so on, and also saying the times table in words: "One times two is two; two times two is four …"

Use silly voices. Move around. Do a silly walk or even a dance. All these things will help make each times table memorable!

## Make times tables relevant

It's always easier to persevere at something if there is a reason. The reward of learning the times tables is how much easier it makes it to work out number problems. So show your child how you work out everyday number problems. Tell your child how to use multiplication to work out the cost of cinema tickets or multiple packs of sweets, for example. Get your child involved in working out how much three of something costs. Help with using the strategy that works for them – repeated addition or a number line. As your child becomes more confident, chant the relevant times table together to get to the answer.

# CONGRATULATIONS

_____
(Name)

has completed the Disney Learning Workbook:

## Times Tables

Presented on

_____
(Date)

_____
(Parent's Signature)